FIRST YEAR
HENLE LATIN

Units I-II

Quizzes & Tests

Written by Martin Cothran
Edited by Michael Simpson

MEMORIA PRESS

www.MemoriaPress.com

FIRST YEAR HENLE LATIN QUIZZES & TESTS FOR UNITS I - II

Martin Cothran
edited by Michael Simpson

ISBN 978-1-61538-140-1

First Edition © 2012 Memoria Press

Table of Contents

QUIZZES & TESTS

Week 1 Quiz

(Exercises 1-4, pp. 1-9)

Name_____Date_____

A. Decline

Decline **terra, -ae**:

	Singular	Plural
nom.		
gen.		
dat.		
acc.		
abl.		

B. Translate

Give the grammatical form of the following nouns and translate them into English:

	Case	Number	Meaning
terrarum			
portae			
Mariae			
nautas			
victoriis			
silvas			
gloriam			

C. Grammar

1. All nouns that end in –*ae* in the genitive singular are in the _____ declension.

Week 2 Quiz
(Exercises 5-7, pp. 9-15)

Name_____ Date_____

A. Decline

Decline **terra, -ae**:

	Singular	Plural
nom.		
gen.		
dat.		
acc.		
abl.		

B. Translate

Give the grammatical form of the following nouns and translate them into English:

	Case	Number	Meaning
terris			
portas			
Mariā			
nautae			
victoria			
silvas			
gloriam			

Translate the following:

1. Nautae terram laudant._____

2. The sailors see the province. _____

C. Grammar

1. The subject of a finite verb is in the _____case.

2. A finite verb agrees with its subject in _____ and _____ .

3. The direct object of a transitive verb is in the _____case.

Week 3 Quiz

(Exercises 8-11, pp. 16-18)

Name_____Date_____

A. Decline

Decline **servus, -i**:

	Singular	Plural
nom.		
gen.		
dat.		
acc.		
abl.		

B. Translate

Give the grammatical form of the following nouns and translate them into English:

	Case	Number	Meaning
filiis			
Christum			
Christiani			
amicos			
servo			
Deo			
amicorum			

Translate the following:

1. Gloria provinciae _____

2. The sailors' victory _____

C. Grammar

1. All nouns that end in –*i* in the genitive singular are in the _____ declension.

2. The possessive case and many English of-phrases are translated by the _____case.

Week 4 Quiz

(Exercises 11-14, pp. 18-20)

Name_____Date_____

A. Decline

Decline **servus, -i**:

	Singular	Plural
nom.		
gen.		
dat.		
acc.		
abl.		

B. Grammar

1. All nouns that end in –*i* in the genitive singular are in the _____ declension.

C. Translate

Give the grammatical form of the following nouns and translate them into English:

	Case	Number	Meaning
filiorum			
amico			
Dei			
servum			
Christus			
filii			

Translate the following:

1. gloria Dei_____

2. Christiani orant._____

3. Christians praise the Son of Mary. _____

Week 5 Quiz

(Exercises 15-18, pp. 20-22)

Name_____Date_____

A. Decline

Decline **bellum, -i**:

	Singular	Plural
nom.		
gen.		
dat.		
acc.		
abl.		

B. Translate

Give the grammatical form of the following nouns and translate them into English:

	Case	Number	Meaning
caelo			
periculis			
regna			
praemio			
bellorum			
imperium			

Translate the following:

1. Regnum Christi _____

2. Nautae caelum et terram vident. _____

3. Deus bella non laudat._____

Week 6 Quiz

(Exercises 19-21, pp. 22-24)

Name_____Date_____

A. Decline

Decline **gladius, -i**:

	Singular	Plural
nom.		
gen.		
dat.		
acc.		
abl.		

B. Grammar

1. The indirect object is put in the_____case.

C. Translate

Translate the following:

1. Christus Deo gloriam dedit._____

2. Nautae amicis victoriam dederunt._____

3. God gave a kingdom to Christ. _____

Week 7 Quiz

Name_____Date_____

(Exercises 22-23, pp. 24-27)

A. Grammar

1. In Latin, some prepositions are followed by the_____case, some by the_____ case.

B. Translate

Give the grammatical form of the following nouns and translate them into English:

	Case	Number	Meaning
oppido			
Galliae			
Gallum			
Romanos			
Roma			

Translate the following expressions:

1. in oppido_____

2. cum Gallo _____

3. propter gloriam Romae_____

4. post victoriam _____

5. after the war _____

6. in the town _____

7. with friends _____

8. on account of the kingdom_____

Week 8 Quiz

(Exercises 24-25, pp. 27-29)

A. The Verb <u>Sum</u>

Give the forms of the verb **sum**.	

B. Translate

Translate the following expressions:

1. Estis filii Dei. _____

2. Christ is the Son of God._____

Week 9 Review Test

(Exercises 26-27, pp. 30-34)

A. Translate

Videtis Christianos. Videtis Mariam et Christum et Deum. Christiani in terrā sunt, sed Christus et Maria in Caelo cum Deo sunt. Pericula Christianorum in terrā sunt, sed praemia sunt in Caelo. Itaque Christiani in terrā orant. Maria cum Christianis orat quod Christiani filii Mariae sunt. Christiani Mariam laudant quod Christus est Filius Mariae. Christum laudant quod Filius Dei est.

_____

_____

_____

_____

_____

_____

_____

Week 10 Quiz

Name_____ Date_____

A. Decline

Decline **lex**:

	Singular	Plural
nom.		
gen.		
dat.		
acc.		
abl.		

B. Grammar

1. All nouns whose genitive singular ends in *–is* belong to the _____ declension.

C. Translate

Give the grammatical form of the following nouns and translate them into English:

	Case	Number	Meaning
lux			
regum			
duci			
leges			
hominem			
imperatoribus			
veritatis			
legibus			
regem			
duces			

Translate the following:

1. lux veritatis_____

2. behind the king _____

3. Christus est Rex Regum. _____

4. The commander-in-chief does not praise the leader of the Gauls.

    _____

    _____

Week 11 Quiz

(Exercises 36-39, pp. 38-42)

A. Grammar

1. An appositive agrees with its noun in _____ and _____ .

B. Translate

Give the grammatical form of the following nouns and translate them into English:

	Case	Number	Meaning
Caesare			
salutis			
voces			
regi			
lucem			
hominibus			
imperatorum			
veritas			

Translate the following:

1. Galli Caesari, imperatori Romanorum, praemia non dederunt.

_____

2. Christ, the Son of God, is man on account of the salvation of men.

_____

3. Christiani Christum, Filium Mariae, laudant.

_____

Extra Credit

1. Sanctus Joannes, Christi servus, vocem Christi audivit: "Ego sum Via et Veritas et Vita."

_____

_____

Week 12 Quiz
(Exercises 40-42, pp. 42-44)

Name_____Date_____

A. Decline

Decline **lex**:

	Singular	Plural
nom.		
gen.		
dat.		
acc.		
abl.		

B. Translate

Give the grammatical form of the following nouns and translate them into English:

	Case	Number	Meaning
virtutis			
milites			
pacem			
viae			
populos			

Translate the following:

1. Sunt pericula in silvis Galliae. _____

2. There are roads in Gaul. _____

Extra Credit

1. Vox populi, vox Dei. _____

Week 13 Quiz

(Exercises 43-47, pp. 44-46)

Name_____ Date_____

A. Decline

Decline **pars**:

	Singular	Plural
nom.		
gen.		
dat.		
acc.		
abl.		

B. Translate

Give the grammatical form of the following nouns and translate them into English:

	Case	Number	Meaning
partium			
colli			
hostes			
gentibus			
caedem			

Translate the following:

1. on account of the welfare of the tribe

_____

2. Duces Romanorum hostes in colle vicerunt.

_____

3. Part of the enemy is in the towns, but part is on the hill.

_____

Week 14 Quiz

(Exercises 48-53, pp. 47-50)

A. Decline

Decline **lex**:

	Singular	Plural
nom.		
gen.		
dat.		
acc.		
abl.		

Decline **pars**:

	Singular	Plural
nom.		
gen.		
dat.		
acc.		
abl.		

B. Translate

Give the grammatical form of the following nouns and translate them into English:

	Case	Number	Meaning
fratribus			
partes			
matrum			
clamore			

Translate the following:

1. Christus est rex hominum sed est frater hominum, et Deus est rex hominum sed est pater hominum. Itaque homines sunt fratres. Itaque bellum est caedes fratrum. Itaque Deus et Christus bellum non laudant.

   _____

   _____

   _____

   _____

   _____

2. He heard the shouting of the leading men.

   _____

Extra Credit

1. Miles Christi sum. _____

Week 15 Quiz

(Exercises 54-57, pp. 51-53)

Name_____Date_____

A. Decline

Decline **flumen**:

	Singular	Plural
nom.		
gen.		
dat.		
acc.		
abl.		

B. Translate

Give the grammatical form of the following nouns and translate them into English:

	Case	Number	Meaning
fluminis			
iter			
corpora			
vulneribus			
agmen			
nomini			
flumine			
itinerum			

Translate the following:

1. Propter vulnera miles in agmine non est.

   _____

2. There are bodies and swords in the river.

   _____

Name _____ Date _____

A. Decline

Decline **lex**:

	Singular	Plural
nom.		
gen.		
dat.		
acc.		
abl.		

Decline **pars**:

	Singular	Plural
nom.		
gen.		
dat.		
acc.		
abl.		

Decline **flumen**:

	Singular	Plural
nom.		
gen.		
dat.		
acc.		
abl.		

B. Translate

Translate the following:

1. Propter salutem hominum Christus erat in mundo.

   _____

2. Caesar, imperator Romanorum, cum militibus in Galliā erat.

   _____

3. on account of the salvation of men

   _____

Week 17 Quiz

(Exercises 60, 62-64; pp. 56-57)

A. Decline

Decline **portus**:

	Singular	Plural
nom.		
gen.		
dat.		
acc.		
abl.		

B. Translate

Give the grammatical form of the following nouns and translate them into English:

	Case	Number	Meaning
adventu			
equitatus			
exercitibus			
impetuum			
metui			
spiritum			
portu			
senatūs			

Translate the following:

1. post adventum Christi _____

2. dux equitatūs _____

3. on account of the fear of danger _____

4. with the Spirit of God _____

Name_____ Date_____

A. Translate

Translate the following:

1. Nunc sunt portūs in Gallia.

   _____

2. Caesar cum equitatu in provinciam venit.

   _____

3. Impetum in hostes fecerunt.

   _____

Week 19 Quiz

(Exercises 68-74, pp. 61-63)

Name_____Date_____

A. Decline

Decline **res**:

	Singular	Plural
nom.		
gen.		
dat.		
acc.		
abl.		

B. Translate

Give the grammatical form of the following nouns and translate them into English:

	Case	Number	Meaning
spei			
fidem			
acie			
rerum			
fides			
aciebus			

Translate the following:

1. Milites in acie erant. _____

2. The Senate does not praise the affair. _____

Week 20 Translation Test

(Review)

A. Translate

Translate the following:

1. Mary praises God. _____

2. Deus amicis Marīae praemia dedit.

   _____

3. They did not give the province to the slaves.

   _____

4. Caesar, dux Romanorum, voces Gallorum in silvis audivit.

   _____

   _____

5. Populus ducem militum propter virtutem laudat.

   _____

   _____

6. Christus est rex populuorum et salus hominum quod Deus est.

   _____

   _____

7. In the mountains and the hills _____

8. There are brothers and fathers in the army.

   _____

9. Caesar autem cum exercitu non erat.

   _____

10. Romani in aciem hostium impetum fecerunt.

   _____

   _____

Week 21 Quiz
(Exercises 76-80, pp. 64-69)

Name_____ Date_____

A. Translate

Give the grammatical form of the following nouns and translate them into English:

	Case	Number	Meaning
castrorum			
impedimenta			
gratiam			
gratiis			
copiae (sing.)			
copias			

Translate the following:

Christus, Filius Dei, est filius Mariae. Itaque homo et Deus est. Christus Rex hominum est quod Deus est. In Christo est salus hominum, quod, propter salutem hominum, in mundum venit. Est "Lux Mundi" quod hominibus veritatem dedit. Itaque Christiani gratias Deo et Christo agunt, et Christum, Regem et Imperatorem, laudant.

_____

_____

_____

_____

_____

_____

Week 22 Quiz

(Exercises 75, 81; pp. 65-70)

Name_____Date_____

A. Translate

Give the genitive singular, accusative singular, the gender, and gender rule for the following nouns.

	Gen. S	Acc. S	Gender and Gender Rule
vulnus			
praemium			
regnum			
Gallus			
frater			
collis			

Translate the following:

1. Christians give thanks to God on account of the abundance of the grace of Christ.

   _____

   _____

2. There was a supply of swords in the camp.

   _____

3. The forces of the enemy were not in the province.

   _____

Week 23 Quiz

(Exercises 81-83, pp. 70-71)

Name_____ Date_____

A. Translate

1. Deus, pater hominum, in Caelo est.

   _____

2. Propter salutem hominum Christus homo in terra erat.

   _____

3. Christus, Filius Dei, est rex gentium et populorum.

   _____

4. Spiritus Dei in Christo erat.

   _____

5. Christiani in nomine Christi orant.

   _____

Week 24 Quiz
(Exercises 84-87, pp. 72-75)

Name_____Date_____

A. Grammar

1. Adjectives of _____ generally precede their nouns.

2. Adjectives of _____ generally follow their nouns.

B. Decline

Decline **magnus**:

Singular			Plural		
M	F	N	M	F	N

C. Translate

Translate the following:

1. Multi Christiani in primā acie erant.

   _____

2. Longum agmen in altos montes venit.

   _____

3. Good leaders praise peace.

   _____

4. The long column was in the forest, but the first battle line was on the high mountain.

   _____

Week 25 Quiz

(Exercises 88-90, pp. 75-79)

A. Translate

Translate the following:

1. Legiones Romanae pro castris erant.

   _____

2. Reliqui Galli tuti non erant.

   _____

3. Pro rege bono milites impetum in hostes fecerunt.

   _____

Extra Credit:

1. Gloria Patri et Filio et Spiritui Sancto.

   _____

2. Sanctus, Sanctus, Sanctus, Dominus Deus Exercituum!

   _____

Week 26 Quiz

(Exercises 91-94, pp. 79-81)

Name_____ Date_____

A. Translate

Translate the following:

1. In front of the camp is a deep river.

   _____

2. Caesar was a great general.

   _____

3. Agmen longum erat.

   _____

4. Milites Christiani pro imperatore bono impetum in hostes fecerunt.

   _____

5. Prima legio in acie erat.

   _____

Extra Credit:

1. In nomine Domini _____

2. Domini est terra! Magna est gloria Domini!

   _____

Week 27 Quiz

Name_____Date_____

(Exercises 95-97, pp. 82-84)

A. Grammar

1. All adjectives with *-is, -e* in the nominative singular are declined like _____.

B. Decline

Decline **gravis, -e**:

Singular			Plural		
M	F	N	M	F	N

C. Translate

Translate the following:

1. The danger was serious. _____

2. On account of the common salvation of men, Christ came into the world.

    _____

Week 28 Quiz

Name_____Date_____

A. Decline

Decline **Jesus**:

	Singular
nom.	
gen.	
dat.	
acc.	
abl.	

B. Translate

Translate the following expressions:

1. Galli gloriae cupidi erant.

   _____

2. Filius similis patris est.

   _____

3. Roma est urbs et magna et nobilis.

   _____

4. Caesar et gloriae et imperii cupidus erat.

   _____

Week 29 Quiz

(Exercises 102-103, pp. 88-90)

Name_____ Date_____

A. Translate

Translate the following:

1. There are many bridges on the long and deep rivers of America.

_____

2. The Roman soldiers killed many Christians on account of the name of Jesus.

_____

3. Both sailors and soldiers praise God.

_____

Extra Credit

1. Signum Crucis _____

Week 30 Translation Test
(Review)

Name_____Date_____

A. Translate

Translate the following:

1. The commander-in-chief was in favor with the king on account of the victory.

   _____

   _____

2. Impedimenta non videtis, sed impedimenta sunt in castris.

   _____

   _____

3. Copia gladiorum in castris erat. _____

4. In Christo est salus hominum, quod, propter salutem hominum, in mundum venit.

   _____

   _____

5. Christus est lux mundi. _____

6. In alto flumine _____

7. Cum sancta Maria _____

8. Cum multis militibus _____

9. Post longum iter _____

10. With a good man _____

11. Nauta malus non orat. _____

12. On account of the great fame of Rome, many men praise the laws of the Romans.

    _____

    _____

13. Principes pro muro alto erant. _____

14. There was a great scarcity of grain. _____

15. Via angusta erat. _____

16. Post magnam caedam _____

17. The way was difficult. _____

18. Maria est gratia plena. _____

19. Prima luce equites fortes impetum in reliquos hostes fecerunt.

    _____

    _____

20. Videtis signa legionum et gladios militum.

    _____

21. Christians put all hope and faith in the Lord Jesus Christ.

    _____

    _____

Final Exam

Name_____Date_____

A. Conjugate

Give the forms of the verb **sum**:

	Singular	Plural
1st Person		
2nd Person		
3rd Person		

B. Decline

Decline the 2nd decl. masc. noun **servus**:

	Singular	Plural
nom.		
gen.		
dat.		
acc.		
abl.		

Decline the 3rd declension noun **lex**:

	Singular	Plural
nom.		
gen.		
dat.		
acc.		
abl.		

Decline the 1st and 2nd declension adjective **magnus** in the masculine, feminine, and neuter:

Singular			Plural		
M	F	N	M	F	N

C. Grammar

1. The subject of a verb is in the_____case.

2. The indirect object is put in the_____case.

3. Adjectives agree with their nouns in _____ , _____ ,
   and _____ .

4. The verb usually stands _____ in the sentence.

5. *In* is used with the _____whenever movement or motion is indicated.

Final Exam

D. Translate

Give the form* of the following nouns and translate them into English:

	Form	Meaning
gratiae		
muri		
regnum		
legionibus		
colli		
legione		
filii		
militem		
provinciam		
pericula		

*Giving the form involves giving the gender, number, and grammatical case. Some words have multiple answers. (You only need to give one.)

Translate the following:

1. Propter bellum, nautae orant.

   _____

2. Jesus pro omnibus hominibus orat.

   _____

3. Deus praemia omnibus Christianis dedit.

   _____

4. Propter victoriam magnam, Christiani Christum, Filium Dei, laudant.

   _____

5. Sunt multa pericula in silvis Galliae quod milites in Galliā sunt.

   _____

6. Caesar praises the soldiers on account of war.

   _____

7. We praise God because He is good.

   _____

Final Exam

E. Translate

Translate the following:

Christus est rex hominum sed est frater hominum, et Deus est rex hominum sed est pater hominum. Itaque homines sunt fratres. Itaque bellum est caedes fratrum. Itaque Deus et Christus bellum non laudant.

_____

_____

_____

_____

_____

_____

QUIZZES & TESTS ANSWER KEY

Name_____Date_____

A. Decline

Decline **terra, -ae**:

	Singular	Plural
nom.	terra	terrae
gen.	terrae	terrarum
dat.	terrae	terris
acc.	terram	terras
abl.	terrā	terris

B. Translate

Give the grammatical form of the following nouns and translate them into English:

	Case	Number	Meaning
terrarum	genitive	P	of the lands, earths
portae	gen., dat., or nom.	S, S, P	of the gate; to or for the gate; the gates (as a subject)
Mariae	gen., dat., or nom.	S, S, P	of Mary; to or for Mary; Marys (as a subject)
nautas	accusative	P	the sailors (as a direct object)
victoriis	dative or ablative	P	to or for victories; by, with, from victories
silvas	accusative	P	the forests (as a direct object)
gloriam	accusative	S	glory, fame (as a direct object)

C. Grammar

1. All nouns that end in *–ae* in the genitive singular are in the _____first_____ declension.

Quiz 2 Key

Name_____Date_____

A. Decline

Decline **terra, -ae**:

	Singular	Plural
nom.	terra	terrae
gen.	terrae	terrarum
dat.	terrae	terris
acc.	terram	terras
abl.	terrā	terris

B. Translate

Give the grammatical form of the following nouns and translate them into English:

	Case	Number	Meaning
terris	dative or ablative	P	to or for the lands, earths; by, with, from the lands, earths
portas	accusative	P	the gates (as a direct object)
Mariā	ablative	S	by, with, from Mary
nautae	gen., dat., or nom.	S, S, P	of the sailor; to or for the sailor; the sailors (as a subject)
victora	nominative	S	victory (as a subject)
silvas	accusative	P	the forests (as a direct object)
gloriam	accusative	S	glory, fame (as a direct object)

Translate the following:

1. Nautae terram laudant. _____The sailors praise the land._____

2. The sailors see the province. _Nautae provinciam vident._____

C. Grammar

1. The subject of a finite verb is in the __nominative_____case.

2. A finite verb agrees with its subject in _____person_____ and____number_____ .

3. The direct object of a transitive verb is in the ____accusative_____case.

A. Decline

Decline **servus, -i**:

	Singular	Plural
nom.	servus	servi
gen.	servi	servorum
dat.	servo	servis
acc.	servum	servos
abl.	servo	servis

B. Translate

Give the grammatical form of the following nouns and translate them into English:

	Case	Number	Meaning
filiis	dative or ablative	P	to or for the sons; by, with, from the sons
Christum	accusative	S	Christ (as a direct object)
Christiani	genitive or nominative	S, P	of the Christian; the Christians (as a subject)
amicos	accusative	P	the friends (as a direct object)
servo	dative or ablative	S	to or for the slave, servant; by, with, from the slave, servant
Deo	dative or ablative	S	to or for God; by, with, from God
amicorum	genitive	P	of the friends

Translate the following:

1. Gloria provinciae ___The glory of the province___

2. The sailors' victory ___Victoria nautarum___

C. Grammar

1. All nouns that end in –*i* in the genitive singular are in the _____second_____ declension.

2. The possessive case and many English of-phrases are translated by the __genitive__ case.

Quiz 4 Key

(Exercises 11-14, pp. 18-20)

Name_____ Date_____

A. Decline

Decline **servus, -i**:

	Singular	Plural
nom.	servus	servi
gen.	servi	servorum
dat.	servo	servis
acc.	servum	servos
abl.	servo	servis

B. Grammar

1. All nouns that end in –*i* in the genitive singular are in the _____second_____ declension.

C. Translate

Give the grammatical form of the following nouns and translate them into English:

	Case	Number	Meaning
filiorum	genitive	P	of the sons
amico	dative or ablative	S	to or for the friend; by, with, from the friend
Dei	genitive	S	of God
servum	accusative	S	the slave, servant (as a direct object)
Christus	nominative	S	Christ (as a subject)
filii	genitive or nominative	S, P	of the son; the sons (as a subject)

Translate the following:

1. gloria Dei_____ The glory of God _____

2. Christiani orant._____ The Christians pray. _____

3. Christians praise the Son of Mary. __Christiani Filium Mariae laudant._____

Quiz 5 Key

(Exercises 15-18, pp. 20-22)

Name_____ Date_____

A. Decline

Decline **bellum, -i**:

	Singular	Plural
nom.	bellum	bella
gen.	belli	bellorum
dat.	bello	bellis
acc.	bellum	bella
abl.	bello	bellis

B. Translate

Give the grammatical form of the following nouns and translate them into English:

	Case	Number	Meaning
caelo	dative or ablative	S	to or for heaven, sky; by, with, from heaven, sky
periculis	dative or ablative	P	to or for the dangers; by, with, from the dangers
regna	nom. or acc.	P	kingdoms, royal powers (as subject or direct object)
praemio	dative or ablative	S	to or for the reward; by, with, from the reward
bellorum	genitive	P	of the wars
imperium	nom. or acc.	S	command, power, empire (subject or direct object)

Translate the following:

1. Regnum Christi _____ The kingdom of Christ _____

2. Nautae caelum et terram vident. ___ The sailors see heaven and earth. _____

3. Deus bella non laudat._____ God does not praise wars. _____

Quiz 6 Key

(Exercises 19-21, pp. 22-24)

Name_____ Date_____

A. Decline

Decline **gladius, -i**:

	Singular	Plural
nom.	gladius	gladii
gen.	gladii	gladiorum
dat.	gladio	gladiis
acc.	gladium	gladios
abl.	gladio	gladiis

B. Grammar

1. The indirect object is put in the _____dative_____case.

C. Translate

Translate the following:

1. Christus Deo gloriam dedit._____Christ gave glory to God._____

2. Nautae amicis victoriam dederunt.____The sailors gave the victory to friends._____

3. God gave a kingdom to Christ. _____Deus regnum Christo dedit._____

Quiz 7 Key

Name_____ Date_____

A. Grammar

1. In Latin, some prepositions are followed by the___ablative_____ case, some by the___accusative_____ case.

B. Translate

Give the grammatical form of the following nouns and translate them into English:

	Case	Number	Meaning
oppido	dative or ablative	S	to or for the town; by, with, from the town
Galliae	genitive or dative	S	to or for Gaul; of Gaul
Gallum	accusative	S	the Gaul (as a direct object)
Romanos	accusative	P	the Romans (as a direct object)
Roma	nominative	S	Rome (as a subject)

Translate the following:

1. in oppido_____in the town_____

2. cum Gallo_____with the Gaul_____

3. propter gloriam Romae_____on account of the glory of Rome_____

4. post victoriam_____after the victory_____

5. after the war_____post bellum_____

6. in the town_____in oppido_____

7. with friends_____cum amicis_____

8. on account of the kingdom___propter regnum_____

Quiz 8 Key

(Exercises 24-25, pp. 27-29)

A. The Verb <u>Sum</u>

Give the forms of the verb <u>sum</u>.	
sum	sumus
es	estis
est	sunt

B. Translate

Translate the following:

1. Estis filii Dei. _____You are sons of God._____

2. Christ is the Son of God. _Christus Filius Dei est._____

Week 9 Review Test Key

Name_____ Date_____

A. Translate

Vidētis Christiānos. Vidētis Mariam et Christum et Deum. Christiānī in terrā sunt, sed Christus et Maria in Caelō cum Deō sunt. Perīcula Christiānōrum in terrā sunt, sed praemia sunt in Caelō. Itaque Christiānī in terrā orant. Maria cum Christiānīs orat quod Christiānī fīliī Mariae sunt. Christiānī Mariam laudant quod Christus est Fīlius Mariae. Christum laudant quod Fīlius Deī est.

You see the Christians. You see Mary and Christ and God. The Christians are on earth, but Christ and Mary are in heaven with God. The dangers of the Christians are on earth, but the rewards are in heaven. Therefore, Christians on earth pray. Mary prays with Christians because Christians are sons of Mary. Christians praise Mary because Christ is the Son of Mary. They praise Christ because He is the Son of God.

Quiz 10 Key

(Exercises 30-35, pp. 35-38)

A. Decline

Decline **lex**:

	Singular	Plural
nom.	lex	leges
gen.	legis	legum
dat.	legi	legibus
acc.	legem	leges
abl.	lege	legibus

B. Grammar

1. All nouns whose genitive singular ends in –is belong to the ___third___ declension.

C. Translate

Give the grammatical form of the following nouns and translate them into English:

	Case	Number	Meaning
lux	nominative	S	light (as a subject)
regum	genitive	P	of the kings
duci	dative	S	to or for the leader
leges	nom. or acc.	P	laws (as a subject or direct object)
hominem	accusative	S	man (as a direct object)
imperatoribus	dative or ablative	P	to or for the commanders-in-chief, generals; by, with, from the commanders-in-chief, generals
veritatis	genitive	S	of the truth
legibus	dative or ablative	P	to or for the laws; by, with, from the laws
regem	accusative	S	king (as a direct object)
duces	nom. or acc.	P	leaders (as a subject or direct object)

Translate the following expressions:

1. lux veritatis _____light of truth_____

2. behind the king _____post regem_____

3. Christus est Rex Regum. ___Christ is King of Kings._____

4. The commander-in-chief does not praise the leader of the Gauls.

    _____Imperator ducem Gallorum non laudat._____

Quiz 11 Key

(Exercises 36-39, pp. 38-42)

Name_____ Date_____

A. Grammar

1. An appositive agrees with its noun in _____case_____ and _____number_____ .

B. Translate

Give the grammatical form of the following nouns and translate them into English:

	Case	Number	Meaning
Caesare	ablative	S	by, with, from Caesar
salutis	genitive	S	of safety, salvation, welfare
voces	nom. or acc.	P	voices (as a subject or direct object)
regi	dative	S	to or for the king
lucem	accusative	S	light (as a direct object)
hominibus	dative or ablative	P	to or for the men; by, with, from the men
imperatorum	genitive	P	of the commanders-in-chief, generals
veritas	nominative	S	truth (as a subject)

Translate the following:

1. Galli Caesari, imperatori Romanorum, praemia non dederunt.
   The Gauls did not give rewards to Caesar, the general of the Romans.

2. Christ, the Son of God, is man on account of the salvation of men.
   Christus, Filius Dei, propter salutem hominum homo est.

3. Christiani Christum, Filium Mariae, laudant.
   Christians praise Christ, the Son of Mary.

Extra Credit

1. Sanctus Joannes, Christi servus, vocem Christi audivit: "Ego sum Via et Veritas et Vita."
   Saint John, the servant of Christ, heard the voice of Christ: "I am the Way and the Truth and the Life."

Quiz 12 Key

Name_____ Date_____

A. Decline

Decline **lex**:

	Singular	Plural
nom.	lex	leges
gen.	legis	legum
dat.	legi	legibus
acc.	legem	leges
abl.	lege	legibus

B. Translate

Give the grammatical form of the following nouns and translate them into English:

	Case	Number	Meaning
virtutis	genitive	S	of courage, virtue
milites	nom. or acc	P	soldiers (as a subject or direct object)
pacem	accusative	S	peace (as a direct object)
viae	gen., dat., or nom.	S, S, P	of the way, to or for the way, ways (as a subject)
populos	accusative	P	the peoples (as a direct object)

Translate the following expressions:

1. Sunt pericula in silvis Galliae. _There are dangers in the forests of Gaul._

2. There are roads in Gaul. _Sunt viae in Galliā._

Extra Credit

1. Vox populi, vox Dei. _The voice of the people, the voice of God._

Quiz 13 Key

Name_____Date_____

A. Decline

Decline **pars**:

	Singular	Plural
nom.	pars	partes
gen.	partis	partium
dat.	parti	partibus
acc.	partem	partes
abl.	parte	partibus

B. Translate

Give the grammatical form of the following nouns and translate them into English:

	Case	Number	Meaning
partium	genitive	P	of the parts
colli	dative	S	to or for the hill
hostes	nom. or acc.	P	the enemy (as a subject or direct object)
gentibus	dative or ablative	P	to or for the tribes; by, with, from the tribes
caedem	accusative	S	the slaughter (as a direct object)

Translate the following:

1. on account of the welfare of the tribe
   propter salutem gentis

2. Duces Romanorum hostes in colle vicerunt.
   The leaders of the Romans conquered the enemy on the hill.

3. Part of the enemy is in the towns, but part is on the hill.
   Pars hostium in oppidis est, sed pars in colle est.

Quiz 14 Key

(Exercises 48-53, pp. 47-50)

A. Decline

Decline **lex**:

	Singular	Plural
nom.	lex	leges
gen.	legis	legum
dat.	legi	legibus
acc.	legem	leges
abl.	lege	legibus

Decline **pars**:

	Singular	Plural
nom.	pars	partes
gen.	partis	partium
dat.	parti	partibus
acc.	partem	partes
abl.	parte	partibus

B. Translate

Give the grammatical form of the following nouns and translate them into English:

	Case	Number	Meaning
fratribus	dative or ablative	P	to or for the brothers; by, with, from the brothers
partes	nom. or acc.	P	parts (as a subject or direct object)
matrum	genitive	P	of the mothers
clamore	ablative	S	by, with, from the shouting, shout

Translate the following:

1. Christus est rex hominum sed est frater hominum, et Deus est rex hominum sed est pater hominum. Itaque homines sunt fratres. Itaque bellum est caedes fratrum. Itaque Deus et Christus bellum non laudant.

   Christ is the King of men, but He is the brother of men, and God is King of men, but He is

   the Father of men. Therefore, men are brothers. Therefore, war is the slaughter of brothers.

   Therefore, God and Christ do not praise war.

2. He heard the shouting of the leading men.

   Clamorem principum audivit.

Extra Credit

1. Miles Christi sum. I am a soldier of Christ.

Quiz 15 Key

(Exercises 54-57, pp. 51-53)

A. Decline

Decline **flumen**:

	Singular	Plural
nom.	flumen	flumina
gen.	fluminis	fluminum
dat.	flumini	fluminibus
acc.	flumen	flumina
abl.	flumine	fluminibus

B. Translate

Give the grammatical form of the following nouns and translate them into English:

	Case	Number	Meaning
fluminis	genitive	S	of the river
iter	nom. or acc.	S	journey, march, route (subject or direct object)
corpora	nom. or acc.	P	bodies (as subject or direct object)
vulneribus	dative or ablative	P	to or for the wounds; by, with, from the wounds
agmen	nom. or acc.	S	column, army (as subject or direct object)
nomini	dative	S	to or for the name
flumine	ablative	S	by, with, from the river
itinerum	genitive	P	of the journeys, marches, routes

Translate the following:

1. Propter vulnera miles in agmine non est.
   On account of wounds, the soldier is not in the column.

2. There are bodies and swords in the river.
   Sunt corpora et gladii in flumine.

Quiz 16 Key

(Exercises 58-60, pp. 53-55)

Name_____Date_____

A. Decline

Decline **lex**:

	Singular	Plural
nom.	lex	leges
gen.	legis	legum
dat.	legi	legibus
acc.	legem	leges
abl.	lege	legibus

Decline **pars**:

	Singular	Plural
nom.	pars	partes
gen.	partis	partium
dat.	parti	partibus
acc.	partem	partes
abl.	parte	partibus

Decline **flumen**:

	Singular	Plural
nom.	flumen	flumina
gen.	fluminis	fluminum
dat.	flumini	fluminibus
acc.	flumen	flumina
abl.	flumine	fluminibus

B. Translate

Translate the following:

1. Propter salutem hominum Christus erat in mundo.

   On account of the salvation of men, Christ was in the world.

2. Caesar, imperator Romanorum, cum militibus in Gallia erat.

   Caesar, commander-in-chief of the Romans, was with (his) soldiers in Gaul.

3. on account of the salvation of men

   propter salutem hominum

Quiz 17 Key

(Exercises 60, 62-64; pp. 56-57)

A. Decline

Decline **portus**:

	Singular	Plural
nom.	portus	portūs
gen.	portūs	portuum
dat.	portui	portibus
acc.	portum	portūs
abl.	portu	portibus

B. Translate

Give the grammatical form of the following nouns and translate them into English:

	Case	Number	Meaning
adventu	ablative	S	by, with, from the arrival, coming
equitatus	nominative	S	cavalry (as a subject)
exercitibus	dative or ablative	P	to or for the armies; by, with, from the armies
impetuum	genitive	P	of the attacks
metui	dative	S	to or for fear
spiritum	accusative	S	spirit, breath (as a direct object)
portu	ablative	S	by, with, from the harbor
senatūs	genitive	S	of the senate
	nom., acc.	P	the senates (as a subject or direct object)

Translate the following:

1. post adventum Christi _____ after the coming of Christ _____

2. dux equitatūs _____ leader of the cavalry _____

3. on account of the fear of danger ___ propter metum periculi _____

4. with the Spirit of God _____ cum Spiritu Dei _____

Quiz 18 Key
(Exercises 65-67, pp. 57-60)

Name_____Date_____

A. Translate

Translate the following:

1. Nunc sunt portūs in Gallia.
   Now there are harbors in Gaul.

2. Caesar cum equitatu in provinciam venit.
   Caesar came with the cavalry into the province.

3. Impetum in hostes fecerunt.
   They made an attack on the enemy.

Name_____Date_____

A. Decline

Decline <u>res</u>:

	Singular	Plural
nom.	res	res
gen.	rei	rerum
dat.	rei	rebus
acc.	rem	res
abl.	re	rebus

B. Translate

Give the grammatical form of the following nouns and translate them into English:

	Case	Number	Meaning
spei	genitive or dative	S	of the hope; to or for the hope
fidem	accusative	S	faith, reliability, faithfulness (as a direct object)
acie	ablative	S	by, with, from the battle line
rerum	genitive	P	of the things, affairs
fides	nominative	S	faith (as a subject) [**fides** is not declined in the plural]
aciebus	dative or ablative	P	to or for the battle line; by, with, from the battle line

Translate the following:

1. Milites in acie erant. _____The soldiers were in the battle line._____

2. The Senate does not praise the affair. __Senatus rem non laudat._____

Name_____ Date_____

A. Translate

Translate the following:

1. Mary praises God. _____Maria Deum laudat._____

2. Deus amicis Marīae praemia dedit.
   God gave rewards to the friends of Mary.

3. They did not give the province to the slaves.
   Servis provinciam non dederunt.

4. Caesar, dux Romanorum, voces Gallorum in silvis audivit.
   Caesar, the leader of the Romans, heard the voices of the Gauls in the forests.

5. Populus ducem militum propter virtutem laudat.
   The people praise the leader of the soldiers on account of (his) courage.

6. Christus est rex populuorum et salus hominum quod Deus est.
   Christ is the King of nations and the salvation of men because He is God.

7. In the mountains and the hills _____In montibus et in collibus_____

8. There are brothers and fathers in the army.
   Sunt fratres et patres in agmine.

9. Caesar autem cum exercitu non erat.
   Caesar, however, was not with the army.

10. Romani in aciem hostium impetum fecerunt.
    The Romans made an attack against the enemy's battle line.

Name_____Date_____

A. Translate

Give the grammatical form of the following nouns and translate them into English:

	Case	Number	Meaning
castrorum	genitive	P	of the camp
impedimenta	nom. or acc.	P	baggage, baggage train (as a subject or direct object)
gratiam	accusative	S	favor, influence, grace (as a direct object)
gratiis	dative or ablative	P	to or for thanks; by, with, from thanks
copiae (sing.)	genitive or dative	S	of the supply/abundance; to, for the supply/abundance
copias	accusative	P	troops, forces (as a direct object)

Translate the following:

Christus, Filius Dei, est filius Mariae. Itaque homo et Deus est. Christus Rex hominum est quod Deus est. In Christo est salus hominum, quod, propter salutem hominum, in mundum venit. Est "Lux Mundi" quod hominibus veritatem dedit. Itaque Christiani gratias Deo et Christo agunt, et Christum, Regem et Imperatorem, laudant.

Christ, the Son of God, is the son of Mary. Therefore, He is man and God. Christ is the King of men because He is God. In Christ is the salvation of men, because, on account of the salvation of men, He came into the world. He is the "Light of the World" because He gave the truth to men. Therefore, Christians give thanks to God and Christ, and they praise Christ, King and General [Commander].

Quiz 22 Key

Name_____ Date_____

(Exercises 75, 81; pp. 65-70)

A. Translate

Give the genitive singular, accusative singular, the gender, and gender rule for the following nouns.

	Gen. S	Acc. S	Gender and Gender Rule
vulnus	vulneris	vulnus	Neuter because it ends in -us (with -ris).
praemium	praemii	praemium	Neuter because it is 2nd declension and its nominative singular form ends in -um.
regnum	regni	regnum	Neuter because it is 2nd declension and its nominative singular form ends in -um.
Gallus	Galli	Gallum	Masculine because it is 2nd declension and its nominative singular form ends in -us. It also refers to an individual male person. Either answer is correct.
frater	fratris	fratrem	Masculine because it refers to an individual male person.
collis	collis	collem	Masculine because it is an exception to *Henle Grammar* No. 50.

Translate the following:

1. Christians give thanks to God on account of the abundance of the grace of Christ.
   Christiani Deo gratias agunt propter copiam gratiae Christi.

2. There was a supply of swords in the camp.
   Erat copia gladiorum in castris.

3. The forces of the enemy were not in the province.
   Copiae hostium in provincia non erant.

Quiz 23 Key

Name _____ Date _____

(Exercises 81-83, pp. 70-71)

A. Translate

1. Deus, Pater hominum, in Caelo est.

   God, the Father of men, is in Heaven. _____

2. Propter salutem hominum Christus homo in terra erat.

   On account of the salvation of men, Christ was a man on earth. _____

3. Christus, Filius Dei, est Rex gentium et populorum.

   Christ, the Son of God, is King of tribes and peoples. _____

4. Spiritus Dei in Christo erat.

   The Spirit of God was in Christ. _____

5. Christiani in nomine Christi orant.

   Christians pray in the name of Christ. _____

Quiz 24 Key

Name_____ Date_____

A. Grammar

1. Adjectives of __quantity__ generally precede their nouns.

2. Adjectives of __quality__ generally follow their nouns.

B. Decline

Decline **magnus**:

Singular			Plural		
M	F	N	M	F	N
magnus	magna	magnum	magni	magnae	magna
magni	magnae	magni	magnorum	magnarum	mangorum
magno	magnae	magno	magnis	magnis	magnis
magnum	magnam	magnum	magnos	magnas	magna
magno	magnā	magno	magnis	magnis	magnis

C. Translate

Translate the following:

1. Multi Christiani in primā acie erant.
   Many Christians were in the first battle line.

2. Longum agmen in altos montes venit.
   The long column came into the high mountains.

3. Good leaders praise peace.
   Duces boni pacem laudant.

4. The long column was in the forest, but the first battle line was on the high mountain.
   Longum agmen in silvis erat, sed prima acies in alto monte erat.

Quiz 25 Key

Name_____ Date_____

A. Translate

Translate the following:

1. Legiones Romanae pro castris erant.

   The Roman legions were in front of the camp.

2. Reliqui Galli tuti non erant.

   The remaining Gauls were not safe.

3. Pro rege bono milites impetum in hostes fecerunt.

   On behalf of the good king, the soldiers made an attack against the enemy.

Extra Credit:

1. Gloria Patri et Filio et Spiritui Sancto.

   Glory to the Father and to the Son and to the Holy Spirit.

2. Sanctus, Sanctus, Sanctus, Dominus Deus Exercituum!

   Holy, Holy, Holy, Lord God of hosts (armies)!

Quiz 26 Key
(Exercises 91-94, pp. 79-81)

Name_____ Date_____

A. Translate

Translate the following:

1. In front of the camp is a deep river.

   Pro castris altum flumen est.

2. Caesar was a great general.

   Caesar magnus imperator erat.

3. Agmen longum erat.

   The column was long.

4. Milites Christiani pro imperatore bono impetum in hostes fecerunt.

   The Christian soldiers made an attack on the enemy for the good general.

5. Prima legio in acie erat.

   The first legion was in the battle line.

Extra Credit:

1. In nomine Domini _____ In the name of the Lord _____

2. Domini est terra! Magna est gloria Domini!

   The earth is the Lord's! Great is the glory of the Lord!

Quiz 27 Key

(Exercises 95-97, pp. 82-84)

A. Grammar

1. All adjectives with *-is, -e* in the nominative singular are declined like_____gravis -e_____ .

B. Decline

Decline **gravis, -e**:

Singular			Plural		
M	F	N	M	F	N
gravis	gravis	grave	graves	graves	gravia
gravis	gravis	gravis	gravium	gravium	gravium
gravi	gravi	gravi	gravibus	gravibus	gravibus
gravem	gravem	grave	graves	graves	gravia
gravi	gravi	gravi	gravibus	gravibus	gravibus

C. Translate

Translate the following:

1. The danger was serious. _Periculum grave erat._____

2. On account of the common salvation of men, Christ came into the world.
   _____Propter salutem communem hominum, Christus in mundum venit._____

Quiz 28 Key

(Exercises 98-101, pp. 85-88)

Name_____ Date_____

A. Decline

Decline **Jesus**:

	Singular
nom.	Jesus
gen.	Jesu
dat.	Jesu
acc.	Jesum
abl.	Jesu

B. Translate

Translate the following:

1. Galli gloriae cupidi erant.

   The Gauls were desirous of glory.

2. Filius similis patris est.

   The son is like the father.

3. Roma est urbs et magna et nobilis.

   Rome is a city both great and noble.

4. Caesar et gloriae et imperii cupidus erat.

   Caesar was desirous of both glory and empire.

Quiz 29 Key

(Exercises 102-103, pp. 88-90)

Name_____Date_____

A. Translate

Translate the following:

1. There are many bridges on the long and deep rivers of America.
    Sunt multi pontes in longis et altis fluminibus in Americā.

2. The Roman soldiers killed many Christians on account of the name of Jesus.
    Milites Romani propter nomen Jesu multos Christianos occiderunt.

3. Both sailors and soldiers praise God.
    Et nautae et milites Deum laudant.

Extra Credit

1. Signum Crucis _____The Sign of the Cross_____

A. Translate

Translate the following:

1. The commander-in-chief was in favor with the king on account of the victory.
   Imperator propter victoriam in gratia cum rege erat.
   _____

2. Impedimenta non videtis, sed impedimenta sunt in castris.
   You do not see the baggage, but the baggage is in the camp.
   _____

3. Copia gladiorum in castris erat. There was an abundance of all things in the camp.

4. In Christo est salus hominum, quod, propter salutem hominum, in mundum venit.
   In Christ is man's salvation, because, on account of the salvation of men, He came into the world.
   _____

5. Christus est lux mundi. Christ is the light of the world.

6. In alto flumine In the deep river

7. Cum sancta Maria With holy Mary

8. Cum multis militibus With many soldiers

9. Post longum iter After a long march

10. With a good man Cum homine bono

11. Nauta malus non orat. The bad sailor does not pray.

12. On account of the great fame of Rome, many men praise the laws of the Romans.
    Propter magnam gloriam Romae multi homines leges Romanorum laudant.
    _____

13. Principes pro muro alto erant. The leading men were in front of a high wall.

14. There was a great scarcity of grain. Erat magna inopia frumenti.

15. Via angusta erat. The road was narrow.

16. Post magnam caedam After a great slaughter

17. The way was difficult. Via erat difficilis.

18. Maria est gratia plena. Mary is full of grace.

19. Prima luce equites fortes impetum in reliquos hostes fecerunt.

    At dawn the brave cavalry made an attack against the rest of the enemy.

20. Videtis signa legionum et gladios militum.

    You see standards of the legion and the swords of the soldiers.

21. Christians put all hope and faith in the Lord Jesus Christ.

    Christians omnem spem et fidem in Domino Jesu Christo posuerunt.

Final Exam Key

Name_____ Date_____

A. Conjugate

Give the forms of the verb **sum**:

	Singular	Plural
1st Person	sum	sumus
2nd Person	es	estis
3rd Person	est	sunt

B. Decline

Decline the 2nd decl. masc. noun **servus**:

	Singular	Plural
nom.	servus	servi
gen.	servi	servorum
dat.	servo	servis
acc.	servum	servos
abl.	servo	servis

Decline the 3rd declension noun **lex**:

	Singular	Plural
nom.	lex	leges
gen.	legis	legum
dat.	legi	legibus
acc.	legem	leges
abl.	lege	legibus

Decline the 1st and 2nd declension adjective **magnus** in the masculine, feminine, and neuter:

Singular			Plural		
M	F	N	M	F	N
magnus	magna	magnum	magni	magnae	magna
magni	magnae	magni	magnorum	magnarum	mangorum
magno	magnae	magno	magnis	magnis	magnis
magnum	magnam	magnum	magnos	magnas	magna
magno	magnā	magno	magnis	magnis	magnis

C. Grammar

1. The subject of a verb is in the _____nominative_____ case.

2. The indirect object is put in the _____dative_____ case.

3. Adjectives agree with their nouns in _____case_____ , _____number_____ , and _____gender_____ .

4. The verb usually stands _____last_____ in the sentence.

5. *In* is used with the _____accusative_____ whenever movement or motion is indicated.

Final Exam Key

D. Translate

Give the form* of the following words and translate:

	Form	Meaning
gratiae	feminine; gen. sing., dat. s., nom. pl.	of grace/favor/influence; to/for grace …; thanks (subject)
muri	masculine; gen. sing., nom. pl.	of the wall, walls (as a subject)
regnum	neuter; nom. sing., acc. sing.	kingdom, royal power (as a subject/direct object)
legionibus	feminine; dat. pl., abl. pl.	to or for the legions; by, with, from the legions
colli	masculine; dat. sing.	to or for the hill
legione	feminine; abl. sing.	by, with, from the legion
filii	masculine; gen. sing., nom. pl.	of the son, sons (as a subject)
militem	masculine; acc. sing.	soldier (as a direct object)
provinciam	feminine; acc. sing.	the province (as a direct object)
pericula	neuter; nom. pl., acc. pl.	dangers (as a subject or direct object)

*Giving the form involves giving the gender, number, and grammatical case. Some words have multiple answers. (You only need to give one.)

Translate the following:

1. Propter bellum, nautae orant.
   On account of the war, the sailors are praying.

2. Jesus pro omnibus hominibus orat.
   Jesus prays for all men.

3. Deus praemia omnibus Christianis dedit.
   God gave rewards to all Christians.

4. Propter victoriam magnam, Christiani Christum, Filium Dei, laudant.
   On account of the great victory, Christians praise Christ, the Son of God.

5. Sunt multa pericula in silvis Galliae quod milites in Galliā sunt.
   There are many dangers in the forests of Gaul because soldiers are in Gaul.

6. Caesar praises the soldiers on account of war.
   Caesar propter bellum milites laudat.

7. We praise God because He is good.
   Quod est bonus Deum laudamus.

Final Exam Key

E. Translate

Translate the following:

Christus est rex hominum sed est frater hominum, et Deus est rex hominum sed est pater hominum. Itaque homines sunt fratres. Itaque bellum est caedes fratrum. Itaque Deus et Christus bellum non laudant.

Christ is the King of men, but He is the brother of men, and God is King of men, but He is the

Father of men. Therefore, men are brothers. Therefore, war is the slaughter of brothers. Therefore,

God and Christ do not praise war.